6/12/85

small

white roaten

S. R. GIFFORD approx 145°

HARTLEY S.L. 450°?

AN AMERICAN GALLERY

VOLUME V

RICHARD YORK GALLERY

21 East 65th Street, New York, New York 10021
212-772-9155 Fax 212-288-0410

An American Gallery, Volume V
Copyright ©1989 by Richard York Gallery

Editors: Eric P. Widing and Richard T. York
Researchers: David B. Dearinger, Nic Madormo, and Evie Terrono
Consultant: Thibault Bouët
Production Assistants: Donna Dempsey and Emma Olson
Photographer: Ali Elai
Printer: Colorcraft Lithographers, Inc.

The issue is not how beautiful the movements but how powerful the punch.

THOMAS SULLY (1783-1872)

1. *Portrait of Mrs. James Robb and Her Daughters, Isabella, Louisa, and Mary*

Oil on canvas, 56⅜ x 45¼ inches
Painted in 1844

RECORDED: Charles Henry Hart, *A Register of Portraits Painted by Thomas Sully 1801-1871* (1909), no. 1419//Edward Biddle and Mantle Fielding, *The Life and Works of Thomas Sully* (1921), p. 260, no. 1479

EX COLL.: Mr. and Mrs. James Robb, New Orleans, Louisiana; by descent to the estate of J. Hampton Robb, Massachusetts

James Robb (1814-1881) moved to New Orleans by the age of twenty-four, ". . . and was a resident of that city for more than two decades, becoming active in the establishment of banking and commercial houses or agencies in New Orleans, St. Louis, Philadelphia, New York, San Francisco, and Liverpool. In New Orleans he set up a private bank, the Bank of James Robb. According to an autobiographical statement, he made six visits to Europe and fifteen to Cuba. In 1842 he became president of the New Orleans Gas Light & Banking Company, and two years later, he headed a newly established gas light company of Havana, Cuba, with the capital, as he observed, divided equally between himself and the queen mother of Spain" [Dumas Malone, ed., *Dictionary of American Biography* (1935), vol. VIII, p. 644].

In 1836 he married Louisa Werninger (1805-1855) and they had three daughters, Isabella, Louisa, and Mary. The Robbs traveled together to Philadelphia in 1844, and Thomas Sully began this painting of the mother and her daughters on August 3rd, finishing the composition on November 21, 1844. At that time Sully was Philadelphia's and America's most esteemed portraitist. A prominent art collector, Robb also acted as patron to other artists such as Thomas Doughty, Asher B. Durand, and Daniel Huntington.

JOSHUA SHAW (about 1777-1860)

2. *View in Western Pennsylvania*

Oil on canvas, 17¾ x 25 inches
Painted by 1848

RECORDED: *Catalogue of the Paintings and Statuary at the Pennsylvania Academy of the Fine Arts* (1848), no. 43//Ann Wells Rutledge, *Cumulative Record of the Exhibition Catalogues, The Pennsylvania Academy of the Fine Arts, 1807-1870* (1955), pp. 202, 367

EXHIBITED: Pennsylvania Academy of the Fine Arts, Philadelphia, 1848, *Stationary Paintings*, no. 48

EX COLL.: Edward Siddons Whelen, Philadelphia, by 1848-1894; to his daughter, Emily Whelen, until 1929; to her nephew, John Frazer; to his sons

One of Joshua Shaw's rare American landscapes, *View in Western Pennsylvania* was exhibited at the Pennsylvania Academy of the Fine Arts in 1848. It bears some resemblance to his *On the Susquehanna* in the collection of the Museum of Fine Arts, Boston.

125°

SAMUEL COLMAN (1832-1920)

3. *Franconia Mountains, New Hampshire*

Oil on canvas, 26 x 36⅜ inches
Signed at lower left: S. COLMAN
Painted by 1853

RECORDED: Wayne Craven, "Samuel Colman (1832-1920): Rediscovered Painter of Far-Away Places," *The American Art Journal,* vol. VIII, no. 1 (May 1976), p. 17//Catherine H. Campbell, *New Hampshire Scenery* (1985), pp. 40, 200//Natalie Spassky, *et. al., American Paintings in the Metropolitan Museum of Art,* vol. II (1985), p. 349

EXHIBITED: National Academy of Design, New York, 1853, *Twenty-Eighth Annual Exhibition,* no. 173//Artists' Fund Society, New York, 1864, *Twelfth Annual Exhibition,* no. 222

EX COLL. private collection, Florida

"Samuel Colman was born in Portland, Maine, in 1832. His father, Samuel Sr., was a prosperous bookseller and publisher, who later moved his family to New York and opened a publishing house. He published illustrated works by some of the most eminent American authors of the day, including Nathaniel Parker Willis and Henry Wadsworth Longfellow, and his establishment was a favorite gathering place for artists and literati. According to Henry T. Tuckerman, Colman's father 'was one of the first tasteful dealers in fine engravings in New York, and his store on Broadway was a unique depository of pictures' [*Book of the Artists* (1870), p. 559]. Young Colman must have become familiar with many examples of engravings and illustrated works, and it is not surprising that he decided to become an artist. He submitted an oil painting entitled *Twilight* (unlocated) to the National Academy of Design in 1851. Little is known of Colman's formal training, although it has frequently been suggested that he was briefly a pupil of Asher B. Durand in the early 1850s. The landscape pictures he chose to exhibit at the National Academy of Design during those years, like *Franconia Mountains, New Hampshire* (unlocated), confirm his concentration on the favorite haunts of the Hudson River school painters. . ." [Meg Perlman, "Samuel Colman," in Natalie Spassky, *et. al., American Paintings in the Metropolitan Museum of Art* (1985), p. 349].

LOUIS REMY MIGNOT (1831-1870)

4. *Winter*

Oil on canvas, 16 x 24 inches
Painted about 1856

EX COLL. private collection, Massachusetts, until 1988

The art-historian Henry Tuckerman writes about Mignot's success with two disparate subjects—tropical and winter landscapes: "At home and abroad his best landscapes have won admiration; in evidence whereof may be cited the ready and liberal prices given even for his studies and sketches at the sale which took place in New York before his departure for Europe, and the warm commendation of the foreign critics . . . . He is a master of color, and some of his atmospheric experiments are wonderful. Compare one of his winter with one of his tropical scenes, and the absolute truth of his manner and method becomes impressive. Of a little picture of the former kind, which was recently exhibited at the British Institution, a critic says in a London journal: 'This is a gem; there is nothing to be said about it, but that it is the most complete little work in the room. We recognize at once its naturalness, not merely in passages, but in the harmonious treatment of the whole.' This estimate applies to many of Mignot's landscapes. He is appreciated by many, however, rather for the brilliancy of his coloring, the mellow and glowing light of his tropical scenes, than on account of the harmony and truth of his more subdued pictures. That the two claims to praise and sympathy should be united in one artist, is no small tribute to his skill and insight" [Henry T. Tuckerman, *Book of the Artists* (1867; reprint, 1966), pp. 563-564].

JAMES E. BUTTERSWORTH (1817-1894)

5. *Flying Cloud off the Needles*

Oil on panel, 12¹⁄₁₆ x 18¹⁄₁₆ inches
Signed at lower right: J E Buttersworth
Painted about 1859-1860

EX COLL.: [Kennedy Galleries, New York, 1960s]; [Coe Kerr Gallery, New York]; private collection, Pennsylvania

The art-historian Harry T. Peters writes about the Flying Cloud in his book on the prints of Currier and Ives: "We come now to the greatest clipper ship of them all, . . . [the] 'Clipper Ship "Flying Cloud."' Measuring 225 feet on the deck, . . . she was built in 1851 by Donald McKay, at East Boston, for Enoch Train of Boston. While she was on the stocks, Train sold her, for double the contract price, to Grinnell, Minturn & Co., of New York . . . Donald McKay was the undoubted master builder of clipper ships, and one of the unrecognized great men of American history. Space does not permit a review of his career. In the words of C.E. Morison, he 'was an unusual combination of artist and scientist, of idealist and practical man of affairs . . . . Experience, character and mathematics self-taught were the firm soil from which the genius of Donald McKay blossomed. He designed every vessel built in his yard, and personally attended to every detail of construction.' The 'Flying Cloud,' on account of her speed, weatherliness, and beauty, was his, and his era's masterpiece. Professor Morison's statement, 'The "Flying Cloud" was our Rheims,' does not seem extravagant. When she made her maiden voyage she was commanded by Captain Josiah Perkins Cressy of Marblehead, then thirty-seven years old, fourteen years as a master, and destined to be remembered as one of the very best men in his profession. Her maiden run to San Francisco, 89 days, 21 hours, was 'the second fastest passage ever made over that course; her fourth voyage, in 13 hours less time, being the record.' On this fourth voyage the 'Flying Cloud' established a permanent record (127 sailing days) from New York to Hong Kong, via San Francisco. A few days out of Hong Kong she ran on a reef and sprang a leak of eleven inches an hour. Captain Cressy kept the pumps going all the way to New York and saved his cargo, worth a million dollars. She later served as a British troop ship, as an emigrant ship to Australia, and as a lumber ship between St. John's and London. She ran ashore near St. John's in 1874 and the following year was burned for her metal" [Harry T. Peters, *Currier & Ives: Printmakers to the American People* (1931), pp. 31-32].

The Flying Cloud is shown here flying the colors of her owners, Grinnell, Minturn & Co. Specifically, she flies from her tallest mast the red-and-white swallow-tail flag of the company's London Line, which the ship sailed in 1859-60.

The Flying Cloud's record breaking voyage of 89 days from New York to San Francisco, set in 1854, was broken only in 1989 by Thursday's Child, making the passage in 80 days around Cape Horn.

SEVERIN ROESEN (about 1815-1872)

6. *Still Life with Basket of Strawberries*

Oil on canvas, 25 x 21¼ inches
Signed at lower right: Roesen
Painted about 1860

EX COLL. descended in the family of the original owner, until 1988

Best known for his table-top compositions of fruit and flowers, Roesen's still lifes are
"the ultimate embodiment of mid-century optimism, representing the richness and
abundance of the land, the profusion of God's bounty in the New World, his blessing
upon the American Eden through this cornucopia of plentitude" [William H. Gerdts,
Painters of the Humble Truth (1981), p. 87].

ALEXANDER WÜST (1837-1876)

7. *Mount Washington, New Hampshire*

Oil on canvas, 52 x 86 inches
Signed at lower right: Alex. Wüst
Painted about 1861

RECORDED: "New Painting for the Art Building," *The Yale Courant,* vol. II, no. 19 (January 23, 1867), p. 151//*Yale College in 1868* (1868), p. 16//Catherine H. Cambell, *New Hampshire Scenery* (1985), p. 178

TO BE RECORDED: Betsy Fahlman, *John Ferguson Weir* (forthcoming, Cambridge University Press)

EXHIBITED: Pennsylvania Academy of the Fine Arts, Philadelphia, 1861, *Annual Exhibition,* no. 148 (possibly included as *Landscape in the White Mountains*)//Yale College, New Haven, Connecticut, 1867, *First Annual Exhibition of the Yale School of the Fine Arts,* no. 126//Yale College, New Haven, Connecticut, 1870, *Second Annual Exhibition of the Yale School of the Fine Arts,* p. 9, no. 19 (corridor)//Yale College, New Haven, Connecticut, 1871, *Third Annual Exhibition of the Yale School of the Fine Arts,* p. 20, no. 19 (corridor)//Yale College, New Haven, Connecticut, 1873, *Fourth Annual Exhibition of the School of the Fine Arts,* p. 7, no. 50//Yale College, New Haven, Connecticut, 1877, *Winter Exhibition*//Hood Museum of Art, Dartmouth College, Hanover, New Hampshire, 1988, *A Sweet Foretaste of Heaven: Artists in the White Mountains 1830-1930,* p. 62, no. 23, illus. in color

EX COLL.: Dr. Robert Wasson Forbes; by gift to Yale College (now Yale University), New Haven, Connecticut, 1867-1965; to [Graham Galleries, New York]; Merchants National Bank, Burlington, Vermont, by 1973; private collection, New Hampshire, until 1989

In 1861 *The Crayon* noted that Alexander Wüst was "engaged on a View of the White Mountains" [Catherine H. Campbell, *New Hampshire Scenery* (1985), p. 177]. That year he exhibited a painting titled *In the White Mountains* at the Pennsylvania Academy of Fine Arts. Both notations may refer to this composition, which a Dr. Robert Wasson Forbes, Yale Class of 1842, gave to his *Alma Mater* in 1867. The gift attracted notice in the local press: "A painting eight feet in length by four and one-half in width, was opened yesterday in the art building. It is from the pencil of Alexander Wüst . . . . It is a view of White Mountain scenery, and is decidedly the finest landscape painting we have seen in this city. It was valued at $3,000.00" ["New Painting for the Art Building," *The Yale Courant,* vol. II, no. 19 (January 23, 1867), p. 151].

JOHN WILLIAM HILL (1812-1879)

8. *The Palisades*

Watercolor on paper, 9⅝ x 16⅛ inches
Signed at lower right: J.W. HILL
Painted about 1865

EX COLL.: private collection, Pennsylvania; [Babcock Galleries, New York]

A Yonkers carpet manufacturer, William S. Cochran, owned the mansion depicted on
the near bank. It overlooks the Tappan Zee, with Nyack visible in the distance. In the
1870's, another Hudson River artist, John Williamson, painted a similar view entitled
Tappan Zee from Lilienthal's, which included the Cochran house and the nearby
Greystone mansion.

JOHN HENRY HILL (1839-1922)

9. *Lake George*

Watercolor on paper, 12¼ x 19¾ inches
Signed and dated at lower left: J. Henry Hill 1867

Ex COLL. private collection

In August of 1867, the date of this watercolor, John Henry Hill first visited Lake George with his brother. By the 1870s, the artist had built a cabin on an island there. From his cabin, he traveled for supplies to Bolton Landing—in summer, by rowboat, in winter, on skates.

ALEXANDER WYANT (1836-1892)

10. *Scene on the Upper Susquehanna*

Oil on canvas, 12 x 26 inches
Signed and dated at lower right: A.H.Wyant/1868

EXHIBITED: National Academy of Design, New York, 1869, *Forty-Fourth Annual Exhibition*, no. 289

EX COLL.: [Babcock Galleries, New York]; to Josephine P. Everette; to Pasadena Art Institute, California (now Norton Simon Museum); Douglas Collins, North Falmouth, Massachusetts, until 1976; to private collection, Brookline, Massachusetts

Wyant painted *Scene on the Upper Susquehanna* in 1868, after he was elected an Associate Member of the National Academy of Design. Upon showing this painting in the Academy's Annual Exhibition the next year, he became an Academician.

ELIHU VEDDER (1836-1923)

11. *A Reverie*

Oil on canvas, 13⅛ x 8 inches
Initialled and dated at lower left: 18V68.70-72.; inscribed on reverse: Elihu Vedder/
Rome 1868/70/72

Ex COLL. private collection, Florida

In the late 1860s, Vedder began to work on a few carefully drawn and richly executed small oils. Joshua Taylor, the art-historian, describes the effect of a composition similar to *A Reverie*: "The antique aspects of the painting serve no particular story; they simply provide a historical detachment or an appealingly sensuous dream. It was to this vaguely designated time and place—historical without specific epoch—that Vedder habitually returned when he wanted to concentrate on physical beauty. The remnants of past grandeur that he now began to collect helped to create an art-historical neverland that provoked reminiscenses of Florence but was unhampered by unnecessary historical information.... This is not a shortcoming but a positive contribution.... There is no story to tell, and yet the senses and the imagination are transported to an arrested eddy of time in which their exercise had full rein" [Joshua C. Taylor, "Perceptions and Digressions," in Joshua C. Taylor, *et. al.*, *Perceptions and Evocations: The Art of Elihu Vedder* (1979), p. 77].

nice pt 6

WILLIAM FREDERICK DE HAAS (1830-1880)

12. *The Maine Coast*

Oil on canvas, 21 x 35¾ inches
Signed and dated at lower right: F. de Haas. '75.

Ex COLL. private collection, Connecticut, until 1988

The artist received his early training at the Academy of Rotterdam and with the painter Van Bosboom at the Hague. He settled in New York in 1854.

Chiefly a painter of coastal scenes, de Haas exhibited at the National Academy of Design beginning in the 1860s. By the 1870s, he frequently showed views of Maine and Newfoundland. His brother, Maurice Frederick Hendrick de Haas, was also a well-known artist specializing in marine scenes.

Biddeford Beach

45°

EDWARD MORAN (1829-1901)

13. *A View in New York Harbor*

Oil on canvas, 30½ x 25⅛ inches
Signed and dated at lower left: Edward Moran 1876; inscribed on reverse:
Edward Moran 1876

EXHIBITED: M.H. de Young Memorial Museum, The Fine Arts Museums of San
Francisco, California, about 1960-1980

EX COLL.: the Honorable Irving M. Scott, San Francisco, California; to his
descendents, until 1982; private collection, New York

"By 1872 Moran had moved to New York, where he exhibited regularly at the National
Academy of Design and became an associate member in 1874. Here ... Moran depicted
tranquil harbor scenes, in which action was minimal, brushwork was less vigorous, and
water and air merged to create a moist, atmospheric haze" [Linda Bantel, "Edward
Moran," in Natalie Spassky, *et. al.*, *American Paintings in the Metropolitan Museum of Art*
(1985) p. 309].

DENNIS MILLER BUNKER (1861-1890)

14. *Portrait of Kenneth R. Cranford*

Oil on canvas, 16¼ x 13 inches
Signed and inscribed at lower right: A Mon Cher Ami/Kenneth Cranford/Dennis
Bunker/Paris 1884

RECORDED: "The Spring Academy," *New York Times* (April 4, 1885), p. 4//"The Spring
Academy Exhibition," *The Art Exchange*, vol. 14 (1885), p. 88//Clarence Cook, "The
National Academy of Design: The Sixtieth Annual Exhibition," *The Studio*, no. 18
(April 11, 1885), pp. 209-210//R.H. Ives Gammell, *Dennis Miller Bunker* (1953),
pp. 48-49, illus. plate 3//Michael Quick, *American Portraiture in the Grand Manner*
(1981), p. 214

EXHIBITED: National Academy of Design, New York, 1885, *Sixtieth Annual Exhibition*,
no. 263 (as *Portrait*, owned by K.R. Cranford)//Museum of Fine Arts, Boston, 1943,
Dennis Miller Bunker, Exhibition of Paintings and Drawings, no. 9

EX COLL.: the artist; to Kenneth R. Cranford, 1884; Mrs. E.N. Vallanigham, by 1943;
private collection, until 1988

Along with Charles Platt, Kenneth Cranford and Dennis Miller Bunker lived and
studied in Paris in the 1880s. According to the artist's historian, "Bunker considered the
Cranford portrait the best thing he had painted up to that time" [R.H. Ives Gammell,
Dennis Miller Bunker (1953), pp. 48-49].

HENRY SIDDONS MOWBRAY (1858-1928)

15. *The Rose Harvest*

Oil on canvas, 14 x 20 inches
Signed and dated at lower right: H. SIDDONS. MOWBRAY.87.

RECORDED: *Art and Artists of All Nations* (1901), p. 315, illus.//Herbert F. Sherwood, ed., *H. Siddons Mowbray: Mural Painter 1858-1928* (1928), p. 140//Elizabeth Broun, *American Paintings and Sculpture in the Fine Arts Building of the World's Columbian Exposition, Chicago, 1893* (unpublished Ph.D. dissertation, University of Kansas, 1976), p. 202, p. xxii, fig. 134, pl. XCIX, illus.//"Manuscript for Mowbray's Autobiography," roll 1898, frame 1187, *Henry Siddons Mowbray Papers,* Archives of American Art, New York

EXHIBITED: Department of Fine Arts, Chicago, Illinois, 1893, *World's Columbian Exposition,* no. 774 (lent by Mr. T. Helman, New York), awarded Gold Prize

EX COLL.: T. Helman, New York, by 1893; Harry J. Applestein, Pittsburgh, Pennsylvania

From around 1880 through the 1890s Mowbray produced a significant group of easel paintings which are primarily of oriental subjects. His "exotic pictures such as 'Rose Harvest' are luscious designs in pinks, reds, mauves, and their complementary greens. The effect is one of saturated sensuality rare in the history of American painting" [Broun, p. 202].

ARTHUR B. CARLES (1882-1952)

16. *Mrs. Carles and Sara*

Oil on canvas, 29⅞ x 24⅝ inches
Painted about 1907

RECORDED: Henry G. Gardiner, *Arthur B. Carles* (1970), p. 142, no. 2, illus.//Barbara
A. Wolanin, "Abstraction (Lost Painting): A Question of Influence," *Arts Exchange I*
(1977), p. 20, illus.

EXHIBITED: The Pennsylvania Academy of the Fine Arts, Philadelphia, 1907, awarded
the First Tappan Prize//The Pennsylvania Academy of the Fine Arts, Philadelphia,
The Corcoran Gallery of Art, Washington, D.C., and National Academy of Design,
New York, 1983-1984, *Arthur B. Carles (1882-1952): Painting with Color,* pp. 30-31,
no. 11, illus.

EX COLL.: the artist; to his daughter, Mercedes Matter, Connecticut; [Judy and Alan
Goffman, Pennsylvania]; to [Janet Fleisher Gallery, Philadelphia]; to private collection,
Pennsylvania

In The Pennsylvania Academy of Fine Arts Competition of 1907, *Mrs. Carles and Sara*
won the artist the Charles Tappan prize, enabling him to spend the subsequent winter
in Europe.

MARSDEN HARTLEY (1878-1943)

17a. *Autumn Cascade I*

Oil on board, 12 x 12 inches
Signed on reverse: Marsden/Hartley
Stamped on reverse: Marsden/Hartley/Auction Sale/New York-1921
Painted about 1909-1910

EXHIBITED: The Anderson Galleries, New York, 1921, *Seventy-five Pictures by James N. Rosenberg and 117 Pictures by Marsden Hartley,* no. H10

EX COLL.: the artist; to [Anderson Galleries, New York, May 17, 1921, lot no. H10]; to Guy Clark; to his daughter, until 1989

17b. *Autumn Cascade II*

Oil on board, 12 x 12 inches
Signed on reverse: Marsden/Hartley
Stamped on reverse: Marsden/Hartley/Auction Sale/New York-1921
Painted about 1909-1910

EXHIBITED: The Anderson Galleries, New York, 1921, *Seventy-five Pictures by James N. Rosenberg and 117 Pictures by Marsden Hartley,* no. H11

EX COLL.: the artist; to [Anderson Galleries, New York, May 17, 1921, lot no. H11]; to Guy Clark; to his daughter, until 1989

In March of 1910, Alfred Stieglitz mounted a group exhibition, *Younger American Painters,* which included three Hartley waterfalls (probably similar, and perhaps the same as the two illustrated here). At that time, Hartley produced small studies measuring just twelve by twelve inches. Barbara Haskell, the art-historian, recounts the artist's approach as Hartley describes it in a letter to his niece:

"I do not sketch much these days for I work almost wholly from the imagination— making pictures entirely from this point of view using the mountains only as backgrounds for ideas ... this is difficult art—almost anybody can paint from nature—it calls for real expert power to create an idea and produce it as one sees it in the mind." The results combined high key, Fauve color with thickly impastoed, distinct brushstrokes which, as in Hartley's 1908-9 paintings, create a flattened, artificial space. In several works, ... the entire expression is conveyed through the brushstroke itself, creating a degree of gestural abstraction that would not be surpassed in America until Abstract Expressionism [Barbara Haskell, *Marsden Hartley* (1980), p. 21].

In 1921 Stieglitz arranged to sell at auction much of Hartley's work, including these paintings. Stieglitz recounts the events in Dorothy Norman's book *An American Seer:*

"At the beginning of the twenties Hartley appeared on the scene in New York one evening and went with O'Keeffe and me to the Chinese restaurant at Columbus Circle. Hartley startled me by sticking his right palm under my nose—a penny in the palm.

continued

17a.

"He said, 'This is all that stands between me and starvation. I know it isn't fair to do this, but I am desperate....'

"O'Keeffe and I were having a very difficult financial problem ourselves. What was I to do? 'What have you in mind?' I asked. 'I would like twelve hundred dollars,' said Hartley....

"'Hartley,' I answered, 'you have about two hundred or more paintings in the vault. Are you ready to give them up in exchange for twelve hundred dollars?' 'Yes.' 'Remember, when they are gone, you will have burnt all your bridges behind you. You won't have a single picture left.'

"The next morning ... I went ... to Mitchell Kennerley, head of the Anderson Galleries. I told him what had occurred. 'Why not have a Hartley auction?' I suggested....

"Kennerley agreed. He was ever the sport, the real article. I explained the plan to Hartley. He said, 'I don't want to see my paintings. I won't attend the sale.'

"With the help of men at the Galleries, we plastered the walls with one hundred and seventeen Hartleys. There were pictures right up to the ceiling. It was an exhilarating room. People came in droves—collectors, art critics and artists amongst them. Even the artists—and others—who had denied Hartley before now seemed to feel he was a versatile and fine painter....

"The men of the Galleries, a wonderful lot of human beings, were all keyed up, as on the day of a race. The room was packed. Standees were rows deep in the hall. Everybody seemed to be present....

"At five minutes before eleven all the Hartleys had been sold. Hartley was present. He sat there and clapped at tense moments, particularly when one of his paintings went for a good price.

"Daniel represented Mr. Howald, his chief customer. 'Poor' people who had been wanting Hartleys for years acquired them for ten and fifteen dollars. To keep things moving, I bid myself. Dr. Albert Barnes, who was in the company of William Glackens, got some handsome Hartleys for about one hundred and fifteen dollars.

"When all was over, the paintings had brought in the sizable amount for the period of five thousand dollars. The entire sum went to Hartley, Kennerley refusing to take any commission. Even complete strangers stood around shaking hands. 'How did you do it?' [Frederick A.] Chapman said, 'I can't believe it.'

"Both Daniel and Montross were greatly impressed. As we came out to the street we could hear voices expressing disbelief that such an auction could occur in America.

"Henry McBride, the critic, was all aglow. Hartley, aquiver, came to me: 'I wish my mother were alive so that she could know this.' The artists, like everybody else, seemed happy....

"Some of us thought this might be a beginning for the American artist—for the unsupported ones of real talent ..." [Dorothy Norman, *Alfred Stieglitz: An American Seer* (1973), pp. 165-167].

17b.

JOHN MARIN (1870-1953)

18. *Palisades on the Hudson*

Watercolor on paper, 13½ x 14⅞ inches
Signed and dated at lower right: Marin 1910; inscribed on reverse: Joseph Marini/
Palisades on Hudson/looking South/(just under/Englewood Cliffs)/(1910)/John Marin

Ex coll.: the artist; to Joseph Marini, Englewood, New Jersey; to his descendents, until
1988

"Spending the years 1905-10 in Europe, and becoming particularly cognizant of current
French art, Marin returned not an eclectic . . . but prepared instead to begin his own
search. . . . Critics of the day praised him, finding in him not feared abstraction but
rather a continuation of Whistler's gentleness; and in fact these early works are wetter,
more tonal, and more realistic than the later ones. But they also go far beyond Whistler
or Prendergast in remaking nature, in seeing the world as made up of flat line and shape
that the artist arbitrates" [Theodore E. Stebbins, Jr., *American Master Drawings and
Watercolors* (1976), p. 305].

WILLIAM GLACKENS (1870-1938)

19. *At the Beach—Bellport*

Oil on canvas, 18 x 24 inches
Painted about 1911-1912

EXHIBITED: North Carolina Museum of Art, Raleigh, 1967, *North Carolina Collects*, no. 207, illus. (as *The Boardwalk*)

EX COLL.: estate of the artist, until 1959; to [Kraushaar Galleries, New York, until 1961]; to private collection, North Carolina, until 1989

"Mr. Glackens has known all along what he was about.... In the several subjects from summer days at Bellport you gain chiefly not a mere recital of the facts of beach and water and boats and bathers but rather a composite picture of the artist's mental and physical pleasure when he saw and was a part of this outdoor life.... They are painted with essential truth to nature, yet Glackens has quite obviously wished to make these pictures fragments of his own autobiography rather than specimens in physical geography. They are true and they are emotional. If they were not the latter you would turn from them without the enthusiastic feeling of personal participation in their beauty which will almost certainly possess you" ["Glackens' Art Seen in His Recent Works, Canvases Shown at Folsom Gallery and at the Armory," *New York Sun* (March 5, 1913)].

FREDERICK C. FRIESEKE (1874-1934)

20. *Siesta*

Oil on canvas, 23¾ x 23¾ inches
Signed at lower right: F.C. Frieseke
Painted by 1916

EXHIBITED: Macbeth Gallery, New York, 1916, *Recent Paintings by F.C. Frieseke, N.A.*, no. 2//Grand Central Art Galleries, New York, 1939, *Retrospective Exhibition of Paintings by Frederick C. Frieseke*, no. 37

EX COLL.: estate of the artist, until 1966; to private collection

During the First World War, Frieseke lived in Paris. Few works were sent on to New York for sale until his increasing popularity led MacBeth Gallery in 1916 to mount a show, which included *Siesta*. About this time, Frieseke discussed his approach to painting with a newspaper critic:

"I cannot scrape down or repaint a canvas. I must take a new one. I usually make my first notes and impressions with dashes of tempera, then I paint over this with small [strokes] as I have to keep it as pure as possible or the effect of brilliancy will be lost. . . . One should never forget that seeing and producing an effect of nature is not a matter of intellect, but one of feeling" [Frederick Frieseke, interview with Clara T. MacChesney, "Frieseke Tells Some of the Secrets of His Art," *New York Times* (June 7, 1914), in William H. Gerdts, *American Impressionism* (1984), p. 265].

550

ARTHUR G. DOVE (1880-1946)

21. *Calf*

Pastel on linen or very fine canvas, 17¾ x 21½ inches
Signed and inscribed at lower left: To Florence Cane/AGD/Dove
Created about 1911-1912

RECORDED: Frederick S. Wight, *Arthur G. Dove* (1958), p. 36//William Innes Homer,
"Identifying Arthur Dove's 'The Ten Commandments,'" *The American Art Journal*
(Summer 1980), p. 31, illus.//Ann Lee Morgan, *Arthur Dove: Life and Work with a
Catalogue Raisonné* (1984), p. 111, no. 12/13.1, illus

EXHIBITED: Little Galleries of the Photo-Secession ("291"), New York, 1912, *Arthur G.
Dove First Exhibition Anywhere* (probably included)//Whitney Museum of American
Art, New York, 1975-1976, *Arthur Dove*//The Phillips Collection, Washington, D.C.,
The High Museum of Art, Atlanta, Georgia, William Rockhill Nelson Gallery and
Atkins Museum of Fine Arts, Kansas City, Missouri, The Museum of Fine Arts,
Houston, Texas, Columbus Museum of Art, Ohio, Seattle Art Museum, Washington,
The New Milwaukee Art Center, Wisconsin, 1981-1982, *Arthur Dove and Duncan
Phillips: Artist and Patron*, p. 29, 80, 145, no. 16, illus. in color

EX COLL.: the artist; to Florence Cane, Westport, Connecticut; to her widower,
Melville Cane, New York, until 1979; to [Terry Dintenfass, Inc., New York]; to private
collection

"In the last days of February, 1912 . . . [Alfred Stieglitz] presented the Arthur G. Dove
First Exhibition Anywhere that contained a remarkable series of symbolic paintings. 'A
series of abstracts,' Stieglitz said of them. 'The pastels he had ground himself. . . . So the
pictures went up, and of course they were over the heads of the people. . . . They were
beautiful, they were not reminiscent of anyone else'" [Wight, p. 21]. In time they came
to be known as "The Ten Commandments," and while no checklist exists for the show
(which also travelled to the Thurber Galleries in Chicago), present-day scholarship
identifies *Calf* as part of the series.

CHARLES SHEELER (1883-1965)

22. Hallway (Interior)

Oil on canvas, 25¾ x 15⅞ inches
Signed and dated at lower right: Charles Sheeler 1919

RECORDED: Constance Rourke, *Charles Sheeler: Artist in the American Tradition* (1938),
pp. 36, 67, illus.//Martin Friedman, *Charles Sheeler* (1975), pp. 55, 89, illus. in color//
Carol Troyen and Erica E. Hirshler, *Charles Sheeler: Paintings and Drawings* (1987),
pp. 74-75, no. 12, illus. in color

EXHIBITED: de Zayas Gallery, New York, 1920, *Charles Sheeler* (as *The Stairway*)//
National Collection of Fine Arts, Smithsonian Institution, Washington, D.C.,
Philadelphia Museum of Art, Pennsylvania, and Whitney Museum of American Art,
New York, 1968-1969, *Charles Sheeler*, p. 36, no. 20, illus.//Royal Scottish Academy,
Edinburgh and Hayward Gallery, London, 1977, *The Modern Spirit: American Painting
1910-1935*, no. 99//San Francisco Museum of Modern Art, California, St. Louis
Museum of Art, Missouri, Baltimore Museum of Art, Maryland, Des Moines Art
Center, Iowa, and Cleveland Museum of Art, Ohio, 1982-1983, *Images of America:
Precisionist Painting and Modern Photography*, p. 78, fig. 8, illus.//Museum of Fine Arts,
Boston, Whitney Museum of American Art, New York, and Dallas Museum of Art,
Texas, 1987-1988, *Charles Sheeler: Paintings, Drawings, Photographs*, p. 74, no. 12, illus.
in color

EX COLL.: the artist; to private collection, Philadelphia, about 1920-1921; to Mrs.
Edwin Turnbull, Baltimore; to private collection, Texas, until 1988

"In 1919 Sheeler turned from the landscapes and still lifes he had been producing to a
new subject, the domestic interior. It would become one of his major themes. Sheeler
had studied simple rooms and staircases in a series of photographs of his house in
Doylestown, but this hallway, with its gracefully turned newel post belongs to an
unidentified building. This painting was one of the last works Sheeler completed before
moving to New York; he considered it a companion piece for *Flower Forms*.

"Of similar size, the two pictures are the antithesis of each other; *Flower Forms*, with its
dark, luminous color scheme and undulating curves, is rich and sensuous; *Hallway*, with
its flat planes, angular rhythms and thinly applied paint, is almost ascetic. Only the
dark blue of the stairs recalls the deep colors of the other work. Yet despite their visual
dissimilarity, these two paintings share an aesthetic goal, one that became an integral
part of Sheeler's work: to bring a realistic image to the point of abstraction by emphasiz-
ing its innate design and by using arbitrary color" [Troyen and Hirshler, p. 74].

JOSEPH STELLA (1877-1946)

23. *Collage No. 7*

Collage with pasted papers on cardboard, 10 x 7¾ inches
Signed twice at lower right: J. STELLA Joseph Stella
Created about 1921

EXHIBITED: The Museum of Modern Art, New York, 1961, *The Art of Assemblage,*
pp. 32, 164, no. 231, illus. (upside down)//American Embassy, Warsaw, Poland, 1962-
1964, *Art in Embassies* (The International Council of The Museum of Modern Art)

EX COLL.: estate of the artist; to [Rabin and Krueger Gallery, Newark, New Jersey]; to
[Zabriskie Gallery, New York]; to [Robert Schoelkopf Gallery, Ltd., New York]; to
private collection, Texas; to [Robert Schoelkopf Gallery, Ltd., New York]

"Stella's collages," writes Irma B. Jaffe, "have an object quality that belongs entirely to
that art form. It is the reality of the crumpled bit of paper or the torn, dirty cardboard
as an object found and put into place as an artistic act that is asserted" [*Joseph Stella*
(1970), p. 89].

LAURA COOMBS HILLS (1859-1952)

24. *White Petunias*

Pastel on paper, 20 x 17½ inches
Signed at lower left: Laura Hills

EX COLL.: the artist; to William Cushing Loring, Wayland, Massachusetts, until 1959;
to his wife, until 1982; to her daughter

A portrait painter, William Cushing Loring knew Laura Hills through her friend,
Beatrice Hereford, a celebrated actress who also lived in Wayland and established a
summer stock theater there.

"Miss Hills first made an international repute as a miniaturist and then ... turned to
flower painting. Hers were executed in pastel and the blossoms predominate over the
appurtenances. They are organized in radiant color combinations which the pastel
medium facilitated her stating with the maximum clarity without sacrificing the delicate
contours of the petals. Her exhibitions were recurring features of the Boston art scene,
impatient customers lining up outside the doors on opening-day with every picture
generally sold before noon" [R.H. Ives Gammell, *The Boston Painters 1900-1930* (1986),
p. 143].

ROBERT LAURENT (1890-1970)

25. *Acrobat*

Whitewood, H: 21, W: 10½, D: 7⅞ inches
Carved in 1922-1923

RECORDED: Royal Cortissoz, "Random Impressions in Current Exhibits," *New York Times* (March 12, 1922), Part IV, p. 9 (possibly this work)//"Record of Works by Robert Laurent," roll N68-3, frame 152, p. 7, *Robert Laurent Papers*, Archives of American Art, New York

EXHIBITED: Bourgeois Gallery, New York, 1922, *Exhibition of Sculptures by Robert Laurent*, no. 16 (possibly included)//Indiana University, Bloomington, 1961, *Laurent: Fifty Years of Sculpture*, no. 18

EX COLL.: Stefan Hirsch, until 1964; to his widow, until 1988

Throughout his career, Robert Laurent preferred to sculpt directly into the material he had at hand. "My approach to sculpture," he wrote, "is through the simplification of lines and forms in order to express myself with the knowledge obtained from observation and absorption. I have always preferred cutting directly in materials such as stone, wood, and on irregular shapes in any material ... I find [this] always most inspiring.... Generally, I start cutting without a preconceived idea—it keeps me more alert and open to surprises that always develop" [Peter V. Moak, "Robert Laurent (1890-1970)," in *The Robert Laurent Memorial Exhibition*, p. 18].

JOSEPH STELLA (1877-1946)

26. *The Swan*

Oil on canvas, 45 inches (diameter)
Signed at lower center: Joseph Stella
Painted about 1924

RECORDED: Irma B. Jaffe, *Joseph Stella: An Analysis and Interpretation of His Art* (unpublished Ph.D. dissertation, Columbia University, 1966), illus.//Irma B. Jaffe, *Joseph Stella* (1970), p. 198, no. 80//John I.H. Baur, *Joseph Stella* (1971), pp. 47-48, no. 77, illus.

EXHIBITED: Bel R. Berman and Jonas Brown, Newark, New Jersey, 1938, *An Exhibition of Paintings, Sculpture, Ceramics by Foremost American Contemporary Artists*, no. 13, illus.//Whitney Museum of American Art, New York, 1963, *Joseph Stella*, p. 48, no. 19

EX COLL. descended in the family of the artist

In *The Swan* "the gigantic bird fills the upper half of the circular canvas like a heraldic image, while behind it the sky is arbitrarily divided into night and day. The picture has the peculiar optical effect of expanding, perhaps due to the concentric design, until the eye is lost in the light-filled space of Stella's imagination" [Baur, pp. 47-48].

ARTHUR DOVE (1880-1946)

27. *The Seaside*

Assemblage of pinecones, branches, bark, shell of horsehoe crab, painted glass, and oil paint on wood support, 12½ x 10¼ x 3 inches
Created about 1925

RECORDED: Ann Lee Morgan, *Arthur Dove: Life and Work with a Catalogue Raisonné* (1984), p. 150, no. 26.8, illus. in color

EXHIBITED: The Intimate Gallery, New York, 1926, *Arthur Dove* (possibly included)//Donald Morris Gallery, Detroit, Michigan, 1964, *Arthur G. Dove: Oils-Watercolors-Drawings-Collage,* no. 30//University of Maryland Art Gallery, J. Millard Tawes Fine Arts Center, College Park, 1967, *Arthur G. Dove: The Years of Collage,* no. 5//Terry Dintenfass, Inc., New York, 1970, *Arthur G. Dove: Collages*//Washburn Gallery, New York, 1974, *Seven Americans: Arthur G. Dove, Marsden Hartley, John Marin, Charles Demuth, Paul Strand, Georgia O'Keeffe, Alfred Stieglitz*//Delaware Art Museum, Wilmington, 1975, *Avante-Garde Painting and Sculpture in America 1910-1925*//Andrew Crispo Gallery, New York, 1977, *Twelve Americans: Masters of Collage,* no. 93, illus.//Terry Dintenfass, Inc., New York, 1984, *Arthur Dove: Paintings, Watercolors, Drawings, Collages*

EX COLL.: [The Downtown Gallery, New York]; [Terry Dintenfass, Inc., New York]; to private collection

"Between 1924 and 1930, Dove produced a group of about twenty-five assemblages or 'things' as he called them. . . . The materials in Dove's assemblages operate on three different levels of meaning: literal, in which materials convey their original purpose or 'actuality'; formal, dealing with purely visual, abstract qualities of color, texture and composition; metaphoric, in which physical and psychic characteristics of the subject are symbolized. In each assemblage, the objects' original function, their metaphoric connotations and their formal properties combine to produce an entity that both includes and transcends its parts" [Barbara Haskell, *Arthur Dove* (1974), pp. 49, 52].

In the mid-1920s Dove lived on a yacht called the "Mona." He spent his summers sailing Long Island Sound and winters docked at Huntington Harbor, New York.

JOSEPH STELLA (1877-1946)

28. Kathleen Millay

Crayon and metal point on paper, 28 x 22 inches
Signed at lower right: Joseph Stella
Created about 1925

RECORDED: Antonio Porpora, "Giuseppe Stella: un pittore futurista di Basilicata a New York," *Italiani pel Mondo* (September 1926), p. 228, illus.//Irma B. Jaffe, *Joseph Stella* (1970), pp. 199, 209, 251, nos. 105, 333

EXHIBITED: The New Gallery, New York, 1926, *Spring Exhibition, Joseph Stella, Encaustic Paintings*

TO BE EXHIBITED: Amon Carter Museum, Fort Worth, Texas, Museum of Fine Arts, Boston, and National Museum of American Art, Washington, D.C., 1990, *Visual Poetry: The Drawings of Joseph Stella*

EX COLL. descended in the family of the artist

A friend of Stella, Kathleen Millay authored numerous published novels and books of poems. Her sister, the famed poet Edna St. Vincent Millay, was the inspiration for a painting by Stella entitled *The Amazon.* Edna's biographer described Kathleen as "a dark Irish beauty," and she was a well-known figure among Greenwich Village artists and writers.

STEFAN HIRSCH (1899-1964)

29. *Factories, Portsmouth, New Hampshire*

Oil on canvas, 17¼ x 27 inches
Painted about 1930

EXHIBITED: The Phillips Collection, Washington, D.C., 1977, *Stefan Hirsch* (as *Factories, Maine*)//Rosa Esman Gallery, New York, 1979, *Stefan Hirsch, Precisionist Painter,* no. 11//Grand Rapids Art Museum, Michigan, 1979-1980, *Stefan Hirsch, Pioneer Precisionist,* no. 11//Morris Museum of Arts and Sciences, Morristown, New Jersey, 1980, *American Realism of the 20th Century* //Hirschl & Adler Galleries, New York, 1980, *Buildings: Architecture in American Modernism,* no. 45, illus. in color

EX COLL.: the artist; to Robert Laurent, Brooklyn, New York; to his son, John Laurent, until 1979; to [Rosa Esman Gallery, New York, 1979]; to [Hirschl & Adler Galleries, New York]; to private collection, until 1989

"... One is struck immediately by the cool, dispassionate colorforms, juxtaposed with quiet deliberation, which compose his pictures. Sharp lines and curves separate form from form. Natural effects of high light and shadows are absent, so that the forms reveal themselves with crystalline clarity" [Stephan Bourgeois, *A Catalogue of Paintings by Stefan Hirsch* (1927), n.p.].

"In America he was enthralled with the New England landscape and while studying with Hamilton Easter Field he learned to admire the utterly simple design of early farms and furniture, as well as primitive paintings. Fascinated with the countryside in Maine, by the Bullfinch houses in Portsmouth, New Hampshire, by the stark and sometimes foreboding rectangles of factory and city, he became a passionate exponent of American painting. He was regarded as a very promising avant-garde artist, acclaimed by Forbes Watson and Duncan Phillips, and even by the conservative Cortissoz, who admired his sensitive delicacy of draughtmanship. The paintings done during this early period marked him as one of the important Precisionists" [Elsa Rogo, "Stefan Hirsch (1899-1964)," in *Stefan Hirsch* (1977), n.p.].

JOHN KANE (1860-1934)

30. *The Girl I Left Behind*

Oil on board, 15⅜ x 11⅛ inches
Signed at lower right: JOHN KANE; inscribed at lower left: THE GIRL I/LEFT
BEHIND

EX COLL.: Stefan Hirsch, until 1964; to his widow, until 1988

Kane often painted musicians—in this case himself playing his favorite flute, or "tin whistle," which he always carried. A second self-portrait in the collection of the Museum of Modern Art shows Kane bare-chested, in a similarly direct posture.

In 1927, one of Kane's paintings of the Scottish Highlands was accepted into the Carnegie Institute's International Exhibition. It was his first official recognition as an artist. In his autobiography, *Sky Hooks,* he recounts the moment:

> The letters of Mr. Saint-Gaudens always said, "Keep up courage. Keep on." And when he told me the jury had accepted my *Scottish Highlands,* he sent me a letter that would make anyone proud. And as I have said, I have had so many disappointments in life that I wouldn't let such a thing turn my head.

> I wanted to tell someone about it, though. I had no one to tell. I was out of touch with everyone. Mrs. Kane was in Washington and all my people were dead except Joe and I had not heard from him for a long time. Now ever since I came from Scotland I had a little tin whistle. So I pulled it out and played a Highland fling for the little girls to dance to in imagination. "The Forty-Second Highlanders Crossing the Broom Loch" was what I played for those little girls to dance to.

> It was my way of communicating the good news [John Kane, *Sky Hooks: The Autobiography of John Kane*(1938) pp. 154, 157].

The artist's flute is presently in the possession of the Carnegie Institute.

GUY PÈNE DU BOIS (1884-1958)

31. *A Conversation in a Crowd*

Oil on canvas, 20 x 16 inches
Signed and dated at lower left: Guy Pène du Bois/32

Ex coll.: Joseph Shulman; to his estate; to [sale: Sotheby Parke-Bernet, New York, July 10, 1980, lot no. 87C]; private collection, until 1988

Guy Pène du Bois painted *A Conversation in a Crowd* just after his return from Paris, where he saw the art of Picasso, Matisse, and others. "But modernism," writes the critic Royal Cortissoz, "has left him ploughing his own furrow. He was no imitator in his youth and he is no imitator in his prime. It is not enough to say that this is because he knows how to paint. It is also because he uses his brains. . . . It is a vital thing" [*Guy Pène du Bois* (1930), p. 11].

WILL HENRY STEVENS (1881-1949)

32. *Abstraction: Grey*

Pastel on paper, 16¾ x 21¼ inches
Signed and dated at lower center: Stevens '33

EXHIBITED: J. Orville Hanchey Gallery, Northwestern State University, Natchitoches, Louisiana, 1984, *The Natchitoches Art Colony: A Southern Plein-Aire Landscape School*

EX COLL.: the artist; to Inez Chaplin, Natchitoches, Louisiana, in the 1930s; to private collection, Natchitoches, Louisiana, in 1979

"I do not draw a line between objective and non-objective," Stevens writes, "What I have liked in non-objective is, for me, the new experience in design I am permitted when I do not have to tie everything to a base in objective painting. Anyway, I am doing both and will continue to, so long as either seems vital to me" [Bernard Lemann, "Will Henry's Nature: The Pictorial Ideas of W.H. Stevens," TS. (1947-1948), p. 15 archives, Richard York Gallery].

CHARLES G. SHAW (1892-1974)

33. *Pointillist Composition*

Oil with sand on canvas, 36 x 30 inches
Signed at upper left: Shaw; inscribed on reverse: Shaw
Painted in the 1930s

EXHIBITED: Richard York Gallery, New York, 1987, *Charles B. Shaw (1892-1974):
Abstractions of the Thirties,* no. 16

EX COLL.: the artist, until about 1970; to private collection, New York

In an interview, the artist discusses his approach to abstraction:
   "I think in principle I stuck to certain ideas, feelings more, of solidity, impact . . .
   Also in every painting I have ever painted I endeavored to have a balance. It was
   held together. It didn't fall apart and go out to one edge . . . in any abstract work, the
   design is very important" [Charles Shaw, interview by Paul Cummings, April 15,
   1968, transcript, Archives of American Art, pp. 50-51].

AWA TSIREH or Alfonso Roybal (1900-1955)

34. *Green Corn Ceremony*

Gouache on paper, 19¼ x 27¾ inches
Signed at lower right: Awa Tsireh
Painted about 1935

RECORDED: Frederic H. Douglas and Rene d'Harnoncourt, *Indian Art of the United States* (1941), pp. 44-45, illus. in color//*Painting and Sculpture in The Museum of Modern Art* (1942), p. 15//*Painting and Sculpture in The Museum of Modern Art* (1948), pp. 18, 158, illus.//*Painting and Sculpture in The Museum of Modern Art* (1958)//*Painting and Sculpture in The Museum of Modern Art, 1929-1967* (1967), p. 235//*Painting and Sculpture in The Museum of Modern Art* (1977)

EXHIBITED: The Museum of Modern Art, New York, 1940, *Four American Traveling Exhibitions*//The Museum of Modern Art, New York, 1941, *Indian Art of the United States*//The Museum of Modern Art, New York, 1941-1944, *Painting and Sculpture from The Museum Collection*//Greenwich Public Library, Connecticut, 1945, *An Experiment in Research on Corn*//Tate Gallery, London, 1946, *Retrospective Exhibition of American Painting, Organized by the National Gallery of Art, Washington*//The Museum of Modern Art, New York, 1948-1949, *American Paintings from the Museum Collection*//Carlebach Gallery, 1949, *Contemporary Painting by American Indians*//United States Embassy, Oslo, Norway, 1953-1954, *Exhibition in the Embassy*//The Museum of Modern Art, New York, 1961-1964, *America Seen Between the Wars*//Museum of American Folk Art, New York, 1970, *Twentieth Century Folk Art*//Oklahoma Museum of Art, Oklahoma City, 1978, *One Hundred Years of Native American Painting*

EX COLL. The Museum of Modern Art, New York, Abby Aldrich Rockefeller Fund, 330.39, 1939-1988

In New Mexico at the turn of the century an archaeologist named Edgar L. Hewitt hired Indian draftsmen to copy mural fragments discovered in excavations.

"At [Kenneth] Chapman's urging, Hewett brought the most skillful of these draftsmen, Crescencio Martinez and Awa Tsireh back to Santa Fe, where they were given studios in the Palace of the Governors.... More important, however, was the exchange among Pueblo artists in the palace, where an abundance of Indian material was already stored, and their close contact with Anglo painters working in adjacent studios, who were inspired by, and in turn influenced, their Indian colleagues. John Sloan, who occupied studio space in the School of American Research in 1919, when he first came to Santa Fe, was so taken by the Indians' watercolors that he arranged for a group to be shown the next year at the Society of Independent Artists in New York." Awa Tsireh had a profound influence on many other Indian painters, "who were inspired by his wide range of subject matter, delicacy of draftsmanship, color variations, and preservation of indigenous design elements" [William H. Truettner, in *Art in New Mexico, 1900-1945: Paths to Taos and Santa Fe* (1986), pp. 73, 191].

HELEN TORR (1886-1967)

35. *Composition*

Oil on canvas, 22¼ x 26 inches
Signed at upper left: Torr
Painted about 1935

EXHIBITED: Heckscher Museum, Huntington, New York and Graham Gallery, New
York, 1972, *Helen Torr (1886-1967)*, no. 34, illus.//Parrish Art Museum, Southampton,
New York, 1978, *Collection of Eva Ingersoll Gatling*, no. 17

EX COLL.: estate of the artist; to [Graham Gallery, New York, 1967]; to Eva Ingersoll
Gatling, Alabama, until 1987; to private collection, until 1989

A label from Alfred Stieglitz is affixed to the back of *Composition*. It bears the date
1935, the year Helen Torr and her husband, Arthur Dove, sent their paintings to Stieglitz for a planned joint exhibition. The show did not occur, however, though Stieglitz
did produce an exhibition of their art two years before, in 1933.

JOSEPH STELLA (1877-1946)

36. *Tropical Plants (Croton)*

Oil on canvas, 28 x 21 inches
Signed at lower right: Jos. Stella
Painted about 1938

EX COLL. descended in the family of the artist

Stella's life-long interest in the tropics culminated in a trip to Barbados in 1937. In a fanciful note to a tropical Poinsetta, he writes of the renewed emotions and inspiration he found there:

> It was wintertime when I arrived in the tropics, and your high-flaming greeting filled my soul with a start of sudden elation. My drowsing energy, tortured by the cold of northern countries was reawakened as if by magic, set aglow by the radiance of gold and purple light. All the ardor of youth surged through me, with the overflowing, stinging, demanding desire for new conquests in the virgin lands of art [Joseph Stella, "La Poinsettia," in Irma B. Jaffe (trans.), *Joseph Stella* (1970), pp. 117-118].

HANANIAH HARARI (b. 1912)

37. *Smiles*

Oil on canvas, 10 x 11 inches
Signed at lower right: Harari; inscribed on stretcher: "Smiling Pin-ups"/Hananiah Harari/1940

EXHIBITED: Everson Museum of Art of Syracuse and Onondaga County, New York, 1941, *Hananiah Harari*//Art Headquarters, New York, 1942-1943, *Hananiah Harari*//The Museum of Modern Art, New York, 1943, *American Realists and Magic Realists*, p. 65, no. 117//Syracuse University, New York, 1945, *Hananiah Harari*//Martin Diamond Fine Arts, New York, 1981, *Hananiah Harari*//Nardin Fine Arts, Ltd., Cross River, New York, 1986, *Hananiah Harari*

EX COLL. the artist, until 1988

The artist describes *Smiles*: "Random snippets and tearings make their own design. Tension balances between the precisely delineated, arranged images and their background of chance graining patterns. Interplay between positive and negative spaces constitute an abstract force. The multi-hues and whites of the clippings together with the surrounding brown establish the color harmony.

"Such is the 'real' subject of the trompe l'oeil still life painting. But another layer of subject exists in the profusion of pretty-girl portraits—faces for and of themselves. Torn from the popular press, they are explicitly of their time. Though their original purpose was commercial exploitation, in this intimate gallery these images are transformed into private icons proclaiming tender faith in the eternal charm of the smile" [Hananiah Harari, TS., archives, Richard York Gallery].

ILYA BOLOTOWSKY (1907-1981)

38. *Untitled*

Oil on canvas, 30⅜ x 20 inches
Signed and dated at lower right: Ilya Bolotowsky/50

EXHIBITED: Washburn Gallery, New York, 1983, *Bolotowsky: Paintings from 1950*//Robert Schoelkopf Gallery, Ltd., New York, 1988, *Plane Geometry*

EX COLL.: estate of the artist; to [Washburn Gallery, New York]; to [Robert Schoelkopf Gallery, Ltd., New York, 1988]

Bolotowsky's work of the 1930s and early 1940s exhibits affinities to both the biomorphic, Surrealistic shapes of Miró and the Suprematism of Malevich. "Only after the war, in the late forties, would Bolotowsky eliminate the diagonal altogether from his work; beyond that step lay the controlled improvisations of the Neo-Plastic style. In finally coming to Mondrian, Bolotowsky would accept ... a single idiosyncratic, highly personal path out of the decade of the thirties. As a young man he had dreamed of mastering the new language of European art; in Neo-Plasticism he was finally enabled to speak that language with no trace of an accent" [Deborah M. Rosenthal, "Ilya Bolotowsky," in John R. Lane and Susan C. Larsen, eds., *Abstract Painting and Sculpture in America 1927-1944* (1983), p. 54].

INDEX